Spike Press

Home from Home

Sally McKeown
Illustrated by Doug Hatfield

© Spike Press 1992

428-6/232/657.

When Alice got the job at the Swan
Hotel, she had to go on a course.
She had been well trained at home.

She already knew how to answer the
telephone.

26th April

Dear Mr. Crouch

John will not be at school today as he has diarrh diarrh - tummy ache and has been sick all night. He will come back to school as soon as he is better

Yours Sincerely
Mrs. Brown.

She could write formal letters.

She had to learn how to take hotel
bookings.
She already knew that people
often change their minds.

She was very tactful,
even when dealing with the most difficult
of customers.

She knew how important it was
to make the best use of time.

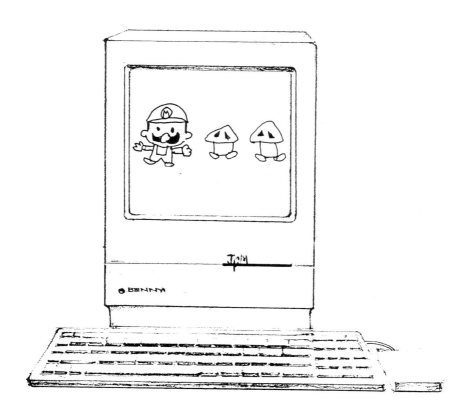

She was an expert on the computer.

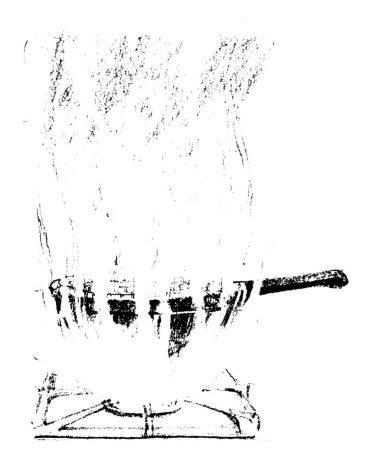

She had learnt about Health and Safety
the hard way.

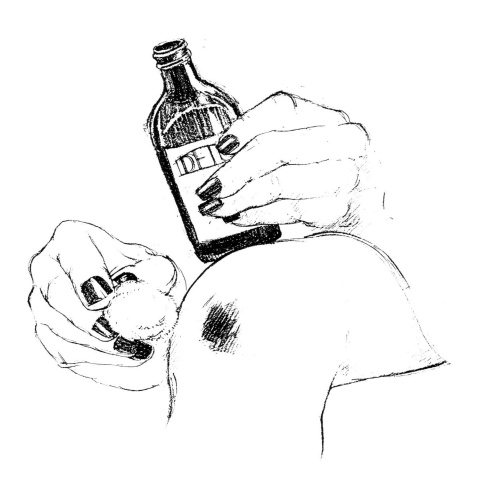

She knew a lot about First Aid.

It was no surprise to Alice
when she passed the course first time.